Pollyanna

LEVEL 4

Original Story by: Eleanor H. Porter
Re-told by: Coleen Degnan-Veness
Series Editor: Melanie Williams

Pearson Education Limited
Edinburgh Gate, Harlow,
Essex CM20 2JE, England
and Associated Companies throughout the world.

ISBN: 978-1-4082-8840-5

This edition first published by Pearson Education Ltd 2014

3 5 7 9 10 8 6 4 2

Text copyright © Pearson Education Ltd 2014

The moral rights of the author have been asserted
in accordance with the Copyright Designs and Patents Act 1988

Printed in Brazil by Docuprint DCPT 220206

Illustrations: Desideria Guicciardini (MIA Milan Illustrations Agency)

All rights reserved; no part of this publication may be reproduced, stored in a retrieval system, or transmitted in any form or by any means, electronic, mechanical, photocopying, recording or otherwise, without the prior written permission of the Publishers.

Published by Pearson Education Ltd

For a complete list of the titles available in the Pearson English Kids Readers series, please go to www.pearsonenglishkidsreaders.com. Alternatively, write to your local Pearson Education office or to Pearson English Readers Marketing Department, Pearson Education, Edinburgh Gate, Harlow, Essex CM202JE, England.

"Nancy, clean the room in the attic," said Miss Polly. "My niece, Pollyanna Whittier, is going to live with me."

"How nice!" cried Nancy.

"Nice? I *must* bring her here," said Miss Polly. "She's eleven years old and an orphan. Her mother, my sister, died years ago. Her father died two weeks ago. I know my duty."

After Nancy went to the attic, Miss Polly thought about her sister, Jennie. Their parents wanted Jennie to marry a rich, older man. But she married a younger man, John Whittier, who had no money. Jennie and her husband left and went south. Jennie wrote a letter to her family after Pollyanna was born. The family never saw Jennie again.

Nancy was angry. "Miss Polly chose the smallest, hottest room for her niece!" she thought.

After cleaning the room, she went to Old Tom, the gardener. They talked about Pollyanna and her parents. Tom told Nancy about a doctor who loved Miss Polly years ago.

"Who is he?" asked Nancy, surprised.

"I'm not telling you. But he lives in town."

Nancy met Pollyanna at the train station.

"Are you Pollyanna?" asked Nancy.

"Yes, I am!" said Pollyanna. "I'm so glad, GLAD, GLAD that I'm here!"

Pollyanna talked all the way home. "I'm so glad that you're my Aunt Polly!" she said at last.

"*I'm* not your aunt!" said Nancy.

"Is there ... an Aunt Polly?" asked Pollyanna.

"Yes, she's waiting for you."

Nancy took Pollyanna into the house. Aunt Polly did not stand up.

"Hello, Pollyanna," said Miss Polly.

"Hello, Aunt Polly!" Pollyanna ran and put her arms round her aunt.

"Stand up straight. I want to look at you," said Aunt Polly.

"Father said …"

"Please don't talk to me about your father," Aunt Polly said, coldly.

Miss Polly took Pollyanna upstairs.

"I can't talk to Aunt Polly about Father," thought Pollyanna. "I'm glad because she doesn't want me to be sad about Father."

"Here's your room," said Aunt Polly. She opened the door.

Pollyanna stopped smiling. She felt scared.

After Aunt Polly left, Pollyanna started to cry. Nancy ran upstairs and took Pollyanna in her arms.

"Don't cry," said Nancy. "Let's put your clothes in the cupboard."

"I don't have many clothes," said Pollyanna. She turned to the window.

"Oh, look at the trees and the river! Now I am *glad* that I have this room!"

"You're nearly always glad," said Nancy.

"That's the game! The glad game!" said Pollyanna. "Father and I played it often."

"It started the day that some women gave me crutches ... I really wanted a doll."

"Crutches!"

"Father said, 'Be glad ... because *you* don't need them!' After that, we found many things which we could be glad about. It's a lovely game!"

"Pollyanna is a lovely child, but so alone," thought Nancy. "She needs a person who can play the game with her."

Weeks later, Aunt Polly gave Pollyanna a prettier bedroom. She started helping Pollyanna with reading. It was her duty.

Pollyanna often walked to town and she always talked to people. Some people started playing the glad game with her.

One afternoon, Nancy was in town with Pollyanna.

"John Pendleton *speaks* to you?" asked Nancy. "He's very rich. He lives alone."

Some days later, Pollyanna met a boy.

"Who are you? Where do you live?" she asked.

"I'm Jimmy Bean. I'm ten years old and I live in the Orphan's Home," said Jimmy. "But I'd like a home with parents."

Pollyanna wanted to find a home for him. She asked Aunt Polly but, sadly, Aunt Polly did not want him.

The next day in Pendleton Woods, Pollyanna saw a man … on the ground!

"Mr. Pendleton!"

"I broke my leg. Get Dr. Chilton!"

Pollyanna ran. Dr. Chilton came quickly and he took Mr. Pendleton home.

Three days later, Pollyanna visited Mr. Pendleton. Dr. Chilton said to the nurse, "This is the girl who plays the glad game! She's famous in this town."

One afternoon, Aunt Polly said, "Pollyanna, take this jelly to Mrs. Snow. She's a poor invalid."

After that, Pollyanna visited Mrs. Snow often. They started playing the glad game. Mrs. Snow felt happier.

Pollyanna also took jelly to Mr. Pendleton.

She said, "Mrs. Snow's a lifelong invalid. *You're* not! Aren't you *glad*!"

"I am," he answered.

Dr. Chilton smiled.

Dr. Chilton gave Pollyanna a ride home. Pollyanna thought, "Dr. Chilton has sad eyes."

"You have the *gladdest* kind of work!" Pollyanna said.

"Gladdest? I see sick, sad people every day!" he answered.

"You *help* them every day!" she said, happily.

Dr. Chilton lived alone. He never had children. But he enjoyed seeing Pollyanna and hearing about her glad game.

Days later, Pollyanna visited Mr. Pendleton again.

He said, "I'd like you to come often. Can you?"

"Yes! There's no school in August," Pollyanna answered.

Mr. Pendleton talked to her about many things. One day, he asked her to live with him. But Pollyanna could not leave her aunt.

Later, Pollyanna thought, "Perhaps Jimmy Bean can live with Mr. Pendleton!"

One afternoon, Mrs. Snow sent Pollyanna for some medicine from Dr. Chilton.

"Is this your home?" Pollyanna asked.

"They're only rooms," said the doctor. "Not a home."

"A man needs a wife, or a child," said Pollyanna. "Mr. Pendleton says, 'Without them, a man doesn't have a home.' *You* need a wife!"

"Getting a wife's not easy," he answered.

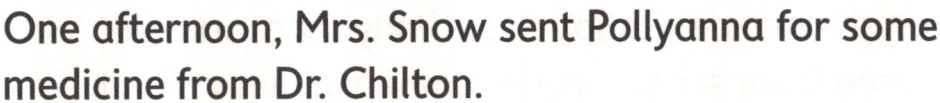

In October, the accident happened. Pollyanna was on her way home from school. A car came suddenly. It hit Pollyanna. A man carried her to Aunt Polly's house. She was not conscious.

Miss Polly called her doctor, Dr. Warren. Nancy ran to the garden and told Old Tom.

"Is she hurt bad?" Tom asked.

"We don't know," Nancy said, crying.

The next day, Pollyanna woke up.

"My legs feel strange," she said.

Aunt Polly nearly cried. The nurse gave Pollyanna some medicine and she went to sleep.

One week later, Pollyanna was conscious again.

"What happened?" she asked.

Aunt Polly told her about the accident.

"I'm hurt, but *not sick*," Pollyanna said. "I'm glad!"

In November, Aunt Polly said, "Dr. Warren's going to bring an important doctor here."

"Is it Dr. Chilton?" asked Pollyanna. She wanted to see Dr. Chilton and she wanted her aunt to meet him.

"No," said Aunt Polly. "It's Dr. Mead."

Dr. Mead told Aunt Polly, "Pollyanna is never going to walk."

"I can *never* be glad again!" Pollyanna thought.

One afternoon, Mr. Pendleton and Jimmy visited Pollyanna.

"Jimmy's living with me now," Mr. Pendleton said.

Jimmy said, "Mr. Pendleton is a wonderful parent!"

Pollyanna was glad!

Some visitors from town told Miss Polly, "We want Pollyanna to play the glad game."

"What's the glad game?" Miss Polly asked Nancy.

Nancy told her. Aunt Polly started playing it with Pollyanna.

At last, Dr. Chilton visited. Aunt Polly knew him years ago.

Dr. Chilton said, "My friend's hospital is for invalids. He can help Pollyanna."

In January, Aunt Polly married Dr. Chilton! Pollyanna was glad!

Then Pollyanna went to the hospital for invalids. After six months, she wrote in a letter, "I can *walk* again!"

They were all glad!

Activity page 1

Before You Read

1 Look at the people in these pictures.
Are they rich, poor, young, old, happy or unhappy?

2 Look at the pictures in your book. Can you see …
a the attic on page 3 or 5? ☐
b an aunt with her niece on page 6 or 7? ☐
c crutches on page 9 or 10? ☐
d a boy who is an orphan on page 11 or 12? ☐
e jelly on page 14 or 15? ☐

Activity page 2

After You Read

1 Which people in the story …
   a have a duty?
   b live alone?
   c play the glad game?
   d are invalids?
   e marry?
   f are orphans?

2 Answer the questions.
   a When did Pollyanna start playing the glad game and why?
   b Why can't Pollyanna tell Aunt Polly about the glad game?
   c What does Dr. Chilton need, says Pollyanna?
   d How does Pollyanna feel about the glad game after she becomes a lifelong invalid?
   e How does Pollyanna change the lives of Mr. Pendleton, Jimmy Bean, Aunt Polly, and Dr. Chilton?

3 At the end of the story, which characters would like to say to Pollyanna …
   a "You live with me and I'm glad!"?
   b "You visited me often after I broke my leg. I'm glad!"?
   c "You told Mr. Pendleton that I needed a home! I'm really glad!"?
   d "Nancy told me about your glad game. I'm glad!"?
   e "Your aunt is going to marry me! I am glad!"?
   f "You can walk again! I'm glad!"?